Contents

Highlights

PuZZle BuZz

Can you find this
buzzing bee?

It is hiding 3 times
on the cover.

COVER ILLUSTRATION BY BRIAN WHITE

Disk Maze

START

Can you help Jake flip his flying disk so Rocky can catch it?
Find a clear path from START to FINISH. Ready, set, flip!

FINISH

Hidden Pictures

Can you find these 12 items hidden in this ice-skating picture?

 teapot

piece of pie

stool

cactus

comb

penny

mushroom

car

fire hydrant

pen

slice of orange

baseball

Dot to Dot

Connect the dots from 1 to 32
to see someone else who
likes the ice and snow.

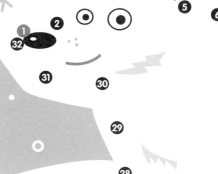

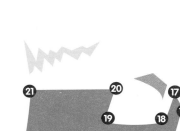

Answer on page 30

Cupcake Search

HAPPY BIRTHDAY LISA!

Lisa is having cupcakes with pink and green icing at her party. Can you find all 16?

Do you know? Are there more cupcakes with green icing or pink icing?

ILLUSTRATION BY DONNA CATANESE

Answer on page 30

Double Pets

The pet shop has something for everyone. These two pictures are a bit different. Add stickers to this page to make them match.

ILLUSTRATION BY LESLIE HARRINGTON

Wiggle Pictures

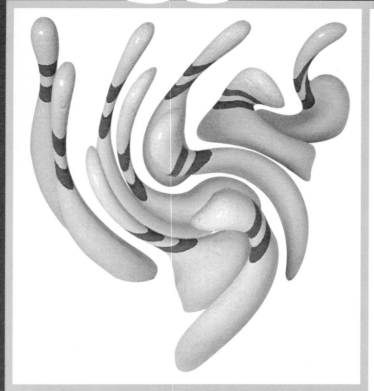

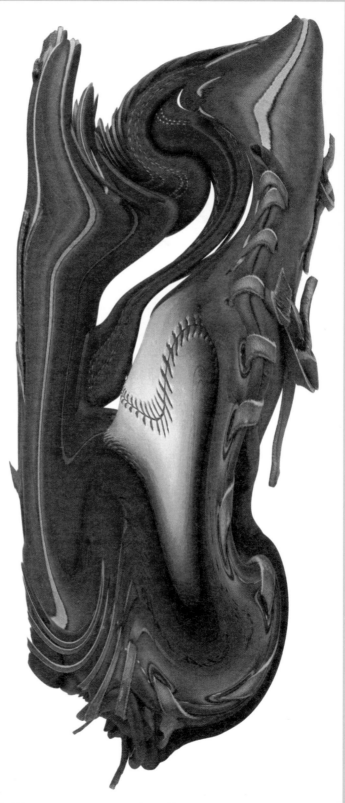

This sports equipment has been twisted and turned. Can you figure out what each one is and name the sport?

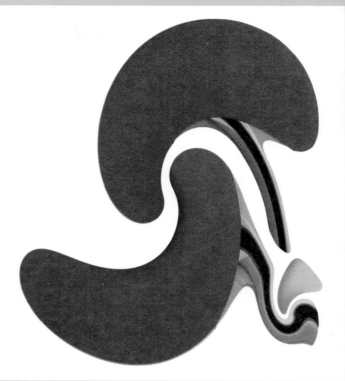

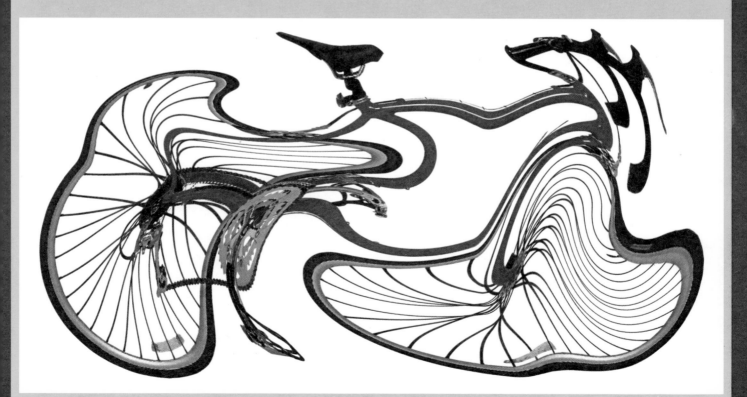

Answer on page 31

Art Starters

Fill-in Fun
Color each space that has a dot to see a turning toy.

Color by Number
Use markers or crayons to color this clown

Highlights **Puzzle Buzz**

Step by Step Follow the steps to draw a turtle.

ILLUSTRATION BY RON ZALME

1.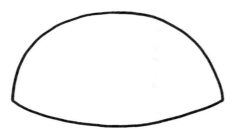

2.

3.

4.

5.

13

Answer on page 31

Match Maker

Every umbrella in the picture has one that looks just like it. Find all 10 matching pairs.

Answer on page 31

What's Wrong?®

Use your stickers to finish the picture. Then see if you can find at least 15 silly things.

266-CS-15

17

Answer on page 31

Try 10

1. Name four rooms you might find in a home.

2. The Spanish word "hermano" means brother.
○ True   ○ False

3. Name two words that rhyme with nail.

5. Name four things that are blue

4. Circle the thing that a magnet might pick up.

6. Circle the flower that has more petals.

7. Chameleons can change color.
○ True   ○ False

8. Name three things you might wear on your hands or fingers.

9. Name five things you might eat for breakfast.

10. Giant pandas come from what country?
○ Kenya   ○ China   ○ Brazil

ILLUSTRATION BY KELLY KENNEDY

19

High Flyers

START

START

These four planes need to land. Follow the paths to see where each one goes.

START

START

Countdown

Answer on page 32

Ready to Roll

ILLUSTRATION BY R MICHAEL PALAN

Kitty Find

The names of 16 cats are hidden in the letters. Some names are across. Others are up and down. We found PUMPKIN. Can you find the rest?

Word List

BUDDY
BUSTER
CUDDLES
DAISY
FUZZY
GINGER
GIZMO
MISTY
PEACHES
PRINCESS
~~PUMPKIN~~
ROCKY
RUSTY
SIMBA
SPIKE
TIGGER

```
X W X M I S T Y V J
V Q P E A C H E S F
P U M P K I N G B U
R O C K Y J W I U Z
I Q G I Z M O N S Z
N R U S T Y Q G T Y
C U D D L E S E E X
E Q T I G G E R R J
S I M B A B U D D Y
S P I K E D A I S Y
```

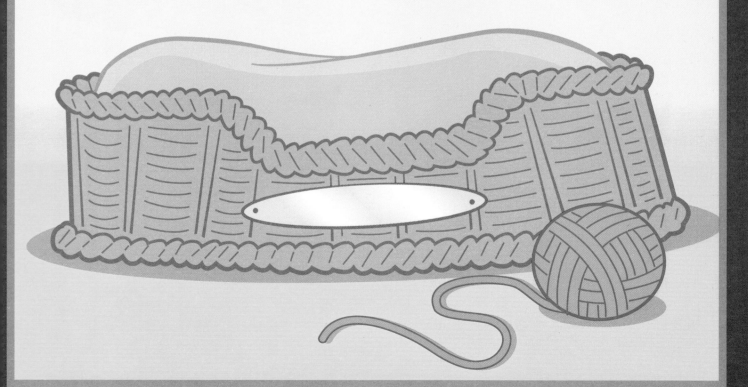

Pretty Kitty Draw a cat and write its name on its bed.

Leaf Code

There are four plant jokes on the next page. Use the leaf code to fill in the letters and finish the jokes. Then tell them to your friends!

A

B

C

E

F

H

I

K

L

N

O

R

S

T

U

Y

What do you call a tree robber?

What do plants like to drink?

Why didn't the tree play checkers?

How can you spot a dogwood tree?

29

Answer on page 32

ILLUSTRATION BY MIKE MORAN

Answers

Cover

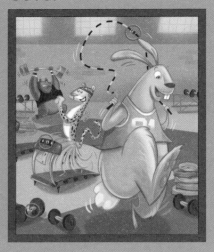

2. Disk Maze

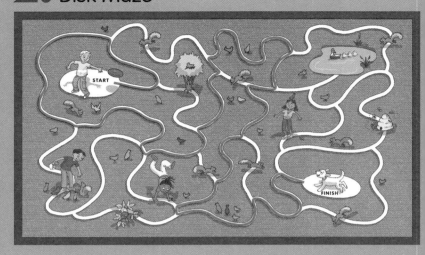

Two of a Kind

4. Hidden Pictures®

5. Dot to Dot

6. Cupcake Search

There are 7 cupcakes with pink icing and 9 cupcakes with green icing, so there are more green ones.

Highlights Puzzle Buzz

Answers

8. Double Pets

10. Wiggle Pictures

bowling

soccer | table tennis

basketball | baseball | bicycle riding

12. Fill-in Fun

It's a pinwheel!

14. Match Maker

16. What's Wrong?®

Here are the things we found. You may have found others.

18. Try 10

1. Kitchen, bedroom, bathroom, and dining room
2. True
3. Snail and pail. Did you think of others?
4. Circle the scissors because magnets pick up things that are metal.
5. The sky, blueberries, blue jeans, and the ocean
6. Circle the flower on the right.
7. True
8. A ring, mittens, gloves
9. Cold cereal, oatmeal, pancakes, waffles, and toast
10. China

Answers

20. High Flyers

22. Countdown

24. Ready to Roll

26. Kitty Find

X W X M I S T Y V J
V Q P E A C H E S F
P U M P K I N G B U
R O C K Y J W I U Z
I Q G I Z M O N S Z
N R U S T Y Q G T Z
C U D D L E S E E X
E Q T I G G E R R J
S I M B A B U D D Y
S P I K E D A I S Y

28. Leaf Code

Q. What do you call a tree robber?
A. **A leaf thief**

Q. What do plants like to drink?
A. **Root beer**

Q. Why didn't the tree play checkers?
A. **It's a chess-nut.**

Q. How can you spot a dogwood tree?
A. **By its bark**

What Is It?

It's a motorbike racer!